I Can Learn
MEGA MATHS
Age 3-5

100 stickers

Activities by Brenda Apsley and Nina Filipek

Illustrated by John Haslam

EGMONT
We bring stories to life

First published in Great Britain in 2004 by Egmont UK Limited
239 Kensington High Street, London W8 6SA
Published in this edition in 2005

© 2007 Egmont UK Limited
ISBN 978 1 4052 2012 5
3 5 7 9 10 8 6 4
Printed in Italy

Contents

Mega Counting 3–5 offers lots of practice in counting skills as described in the Curriculum Guidance for the Foundation Stage. The book reflects the content of the National Curriculum in England and Wales and the National Guidelines for Scotland.

In this book, children will learn to count from zero to twenty, and to:

1. say the names of the numbers;

2. point to pictures (objects) as they are counted;

3. understand that we say one number for each object counted;

4. recognise and write the numbers;

5. match numbers to pictures;

6. make simple calculations, e.g. add more objects to make a given number (addition), share objects equally (division).

The book is aimed at children aged 3 to 5, so the levels of the exercises are progressively more difficult, for example, there are many more calculations in the second half of the book. The content begins at Nursery level and moves up to Reception level. We recommend that your child works through the book in the given order. If he or she starts to struggle or gets bored with any of the pages, skip these questions and return to them on another day when your child is feeling more positive and responsive. Repetition and practice will help build skills and confidence.

Your child can add the 100 fun stickers to the pages of the book as rewards for his or her efforts or use them to decorate pencil cases, posters or other items.

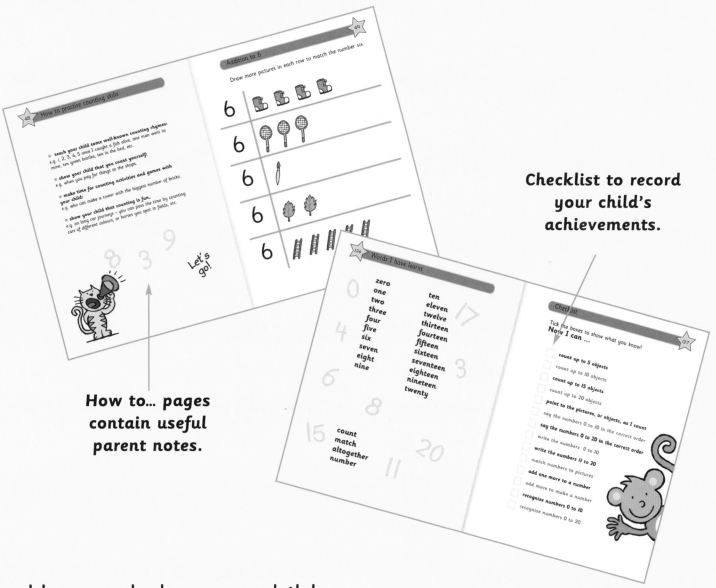

Checklist to record your child's achievements.

How to... pages contain useful parent notes.

How to help your child

Choose a time when your child is alert and eager to learn. Read aloud and point to the instructions on each page. These are written using a simple vocabulary for the age group, but you may also need to explain more fully what your child is being asked to do. Make sure your child can hold a pencil correctly and let your child decide how long he or she wants to work on the book.

Always give lots of encouragement and praise for effort and enjoy the book together.

Zero is a special number.

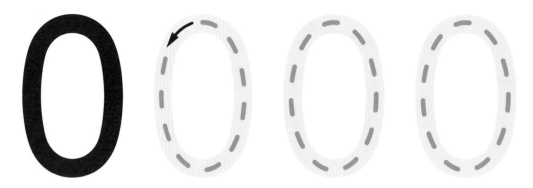

Start at the black arrow and follow the red lines.
Try to keep inside the red shadow.

Can you count any rabbits in the garden?

Can you see any dogs in the kennel?
There are no dogs.

Look at the tree.
Can you count any birds in the tree?
No, there is nothing in the tree.

Look at this tree.
Can you count any birds now? Yes, there is one bird in
the tree.

Follow the lines to write the number one.

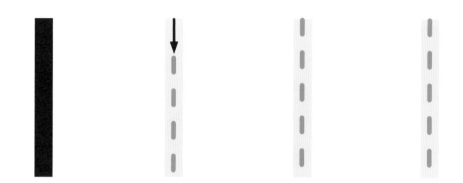

Count one rabbit.

Can you count any dogs in the garden?
Colour the dog.

Can you see one cat hiding behind the kennel?

Follow the lines to write the number two.

Count two planes.

Count two dogs.
Colour two bones.

How many birds in the tree?
Two. There are two birds in the tree.

Count the birds in this tree. How many are there?
There are three birds in the tree.

Follow the lines to write the number three.

Count three spiders.

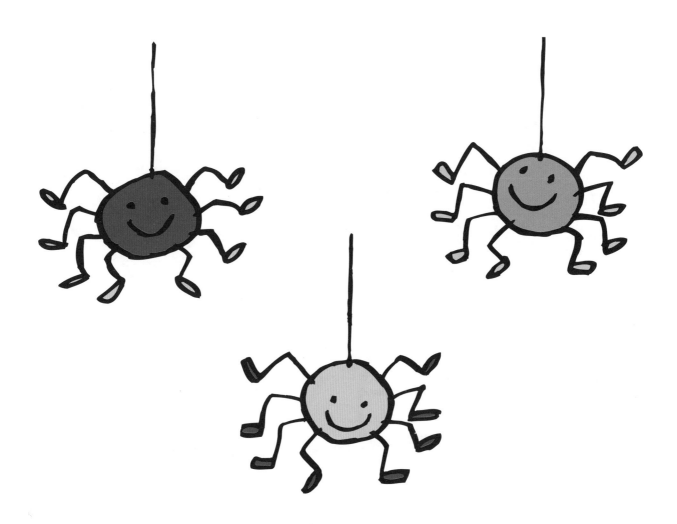

Count three pieces of cheese.
Colour three mice.

Counting isn't just about reciting the numbers 1 to 10 by heart. A well-trained parrot is able to do this, but a parrot has no real understanding of what the numbers actually mean.

To aid your child's understanding of counting and numbers, you can:

- **point to each picture (or object) as it is counted on the page;**
- **explain that we say one number for each picture counted;**
- **talk about the shapes of the numbers as they are written.**

Ring the numbers that match the pictures.

Ring the numbers that match the pictures.

Ring the numbers that match the pictures.

0   1   2   3

0   1   2   3

0   1   2   3

0   1   2   3

Draw three candles on the cake.

Say the truck numbers in order.
Write the numbers on the trucks.

Follow the lines to write the number four.

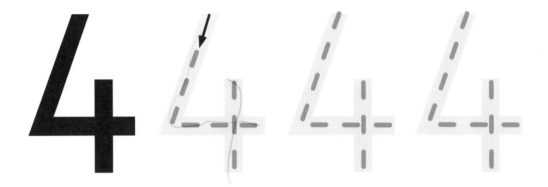

Count four legs.

Count four chairs.
Colour four plates.

How many birds in the tree?
Count four birds.

How many birds now?
Are there five?

Follow the lines to write the number five.

5 5 5 5

Count five petals.

Here are five flowers. Count them.
Colour five plant-pots.

Ring the numbers that match the pictures.

 0 1 2 3 4

 0 1 2 3 4

 0 1 2 3 4

 0 1 2 3 4

Ring the numbers that match the pictures.

0 1 2 3 4 5

0 1 2 3 4 5

0 1 2 3 4 5

0 1 2 3 4 5

Here are five monkeys.
Count and colour them.

Here are five snails.
Write the numbers on their shells.

Say the hat numbers in order.
Write the numbers on the hats.

Count the spots on the dice.
Write the numbers.

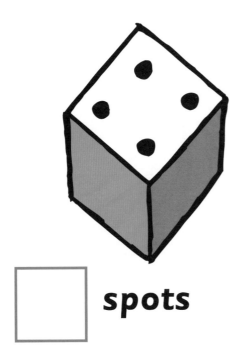

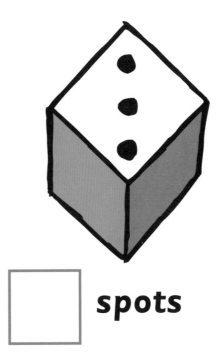

☐ **spots**   ☐ **spots**

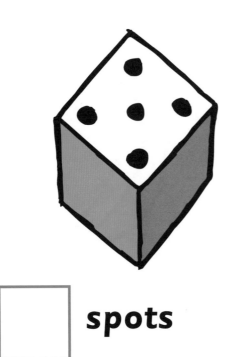

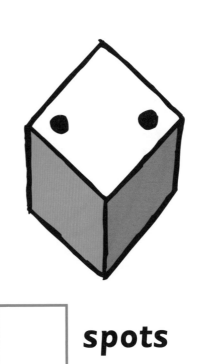

☐ **spots**   ☐ **spots**

Count the bananas.
Write the numbers.

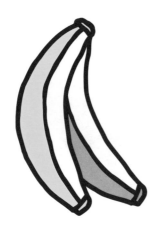

How many? ☐

How many? ☐

How many? ☐

How many? ☐

Draw some more fruit to match each number.

3 pears

5 apples

2 oranges

4 plums

Ring the numbers that match the pictures.

 0 1 2 3 4

 0 1 2 3 4

 0 1 2 3 4

 0 1 2 3 4

Ring the numbers that match the pictures.

 **0 1 2 3 4**

 **0 1 2 3 4**

 **0 1 2 3 4**

 **0 1 2 3 4**

Draw lines to join the pictures to the numbers.

Draw lines to join the pictures to the numbers.

2

5

3

Join the dots. Start at zero.
Colour the tree.

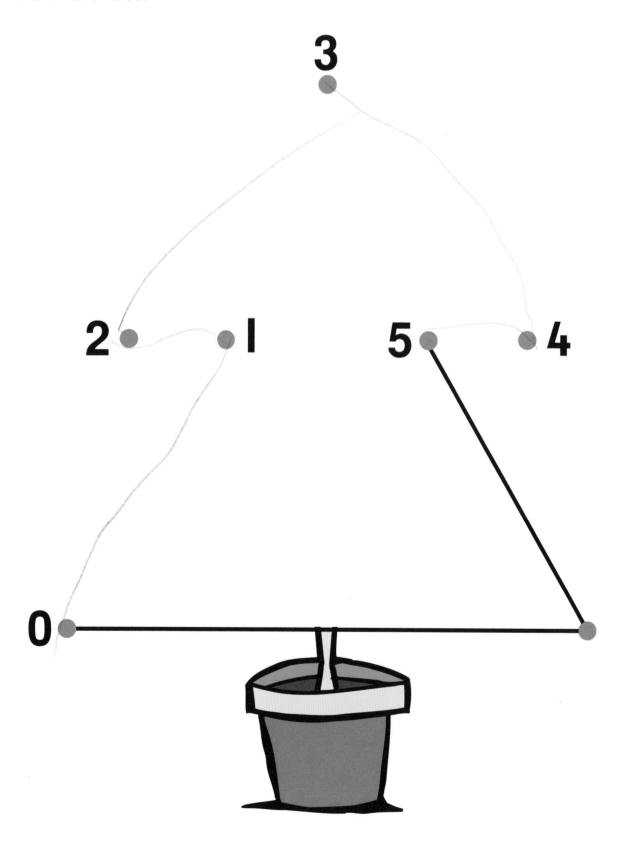

How many birds?

How many starfish?

How many balls?

Count and colour the balls.

Learn to write the number 6

Follow the lines to write the number six.

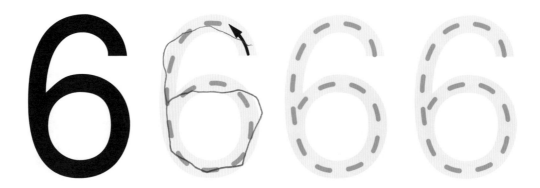

Count six hens.

Count six cups.
Colour six cakes.
How many saucers can you see?

- **teach your child some well-known counting rhymes:**
e.g. 1, 2, 3, 4, 5 once I caught a fish alive, one man went to mow, ten green bottles, ten in the bed, etc.

- **show your child that you count yourself:**
e.g. when you pay for things at the shops.

- **make time for counting activities and games with your child:**
e.g. who can make a tower with the biggest number of bricks.

- **show your child that counting is fun,**
e.g. on long car journeys – you can pass the time by counting cars of different colours, or horses you spot in fields, etc.

Let's go!

Draw more pictures in each row to match the number six.

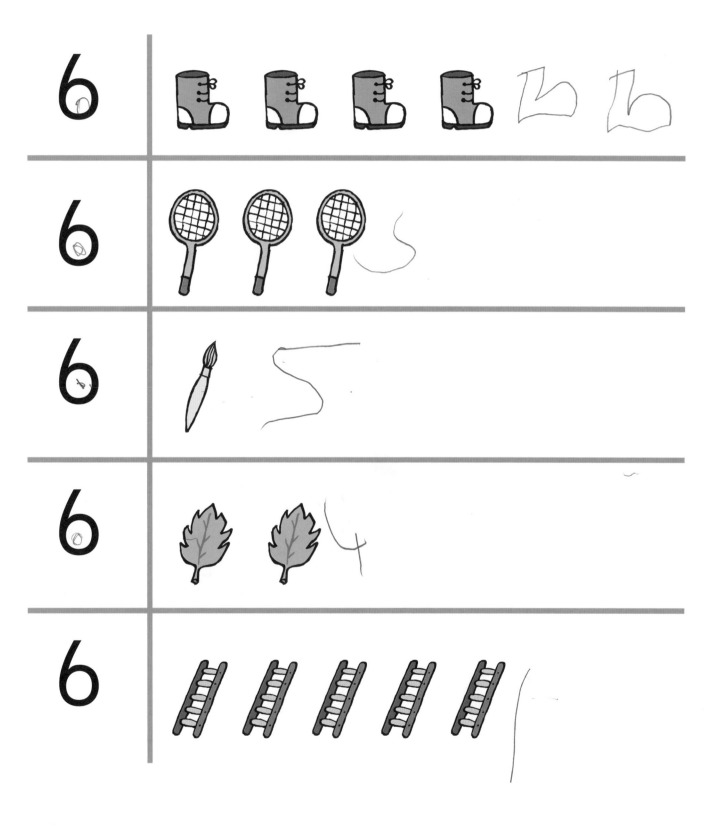

What can you see in the tree?
How many birds can you count?

How many birds in the tree now?
There are seven birds.

Follow the lines to write the number seven.

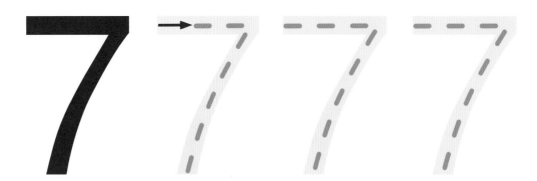

Count seven butterflies.

Count seven shells.
Colour seven fish.

Count the fruit.
Draw lines to join the pictures to the numbers.

7

6

7

6

How many ants?
How many cakes?

Follow the lines to write the number eight.

8 8 8 8

Count eight legs.

Count eight kites then colour them.

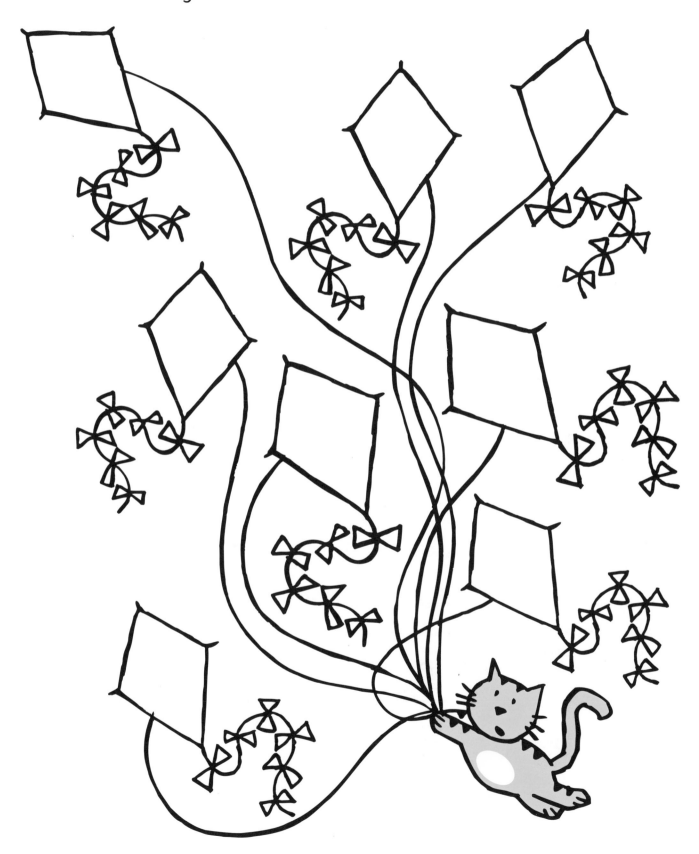

Ring the numbers that match the pictures.

 5 6 7 8

 5 6 7 8

 5 6 7 8

 5 6 7 8

Say the door numbers in order.
Write the numbers on the doors.

How many legs do spiders have?
Draw eight legs on the spider.

Ring the numbers that match the pictures.

6 7 8

6 7 8

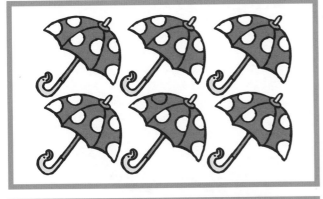

6 7 8

6 7 8

How many birds are in this tree?
There are eight.

How many birds now?
What a lot of birds!
There are nine birds to count now.

Follow the lines to write the number nine.

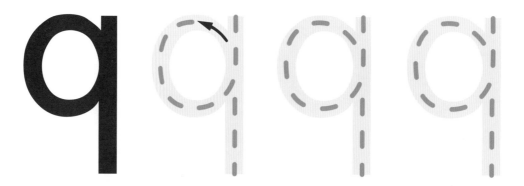

Count nine elephants.

Count nine flowers.
How many bees? Colour them.

Count the dots.
Draw lines to join the dots to the numbers.

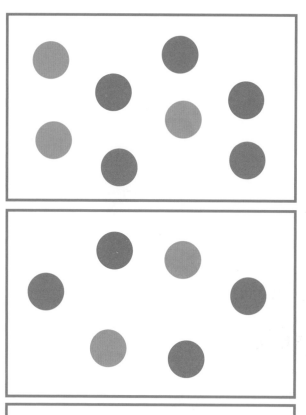

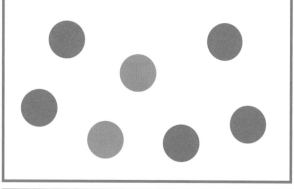

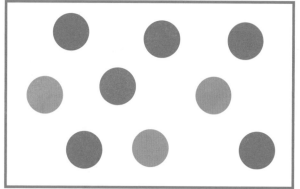

7

9

6

8

Count the bricks.
Write the number for each picture.

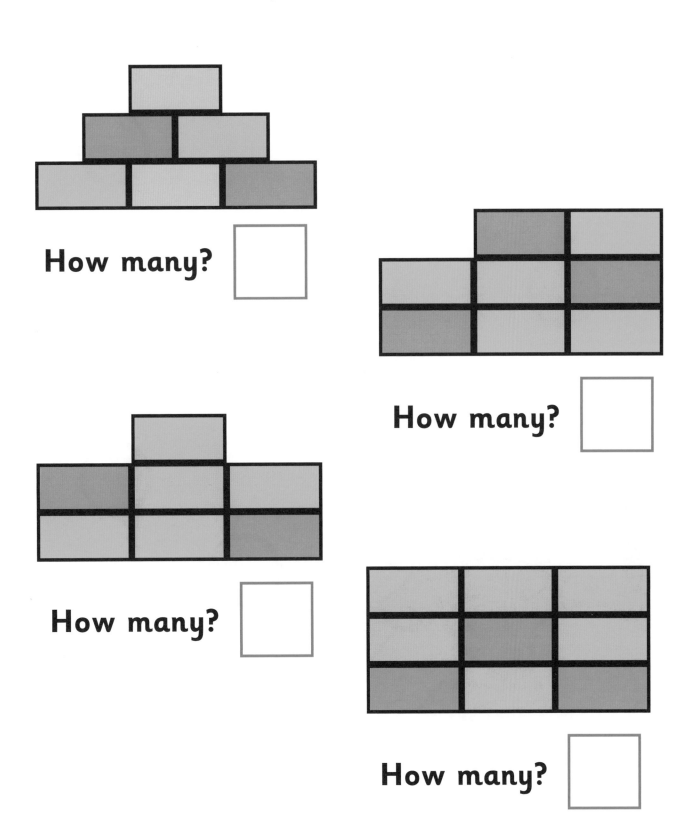

How many?

How many?

How many?

How many?

Draw more balls so that the clown has nine.

How many birds are in the tree now?

Follow the lines to write the number ten.

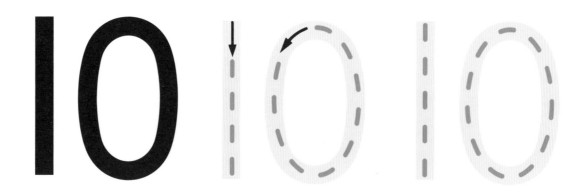

Count ten men.

Count ten birds.
Colour them.

Ring the group of ten buttons.

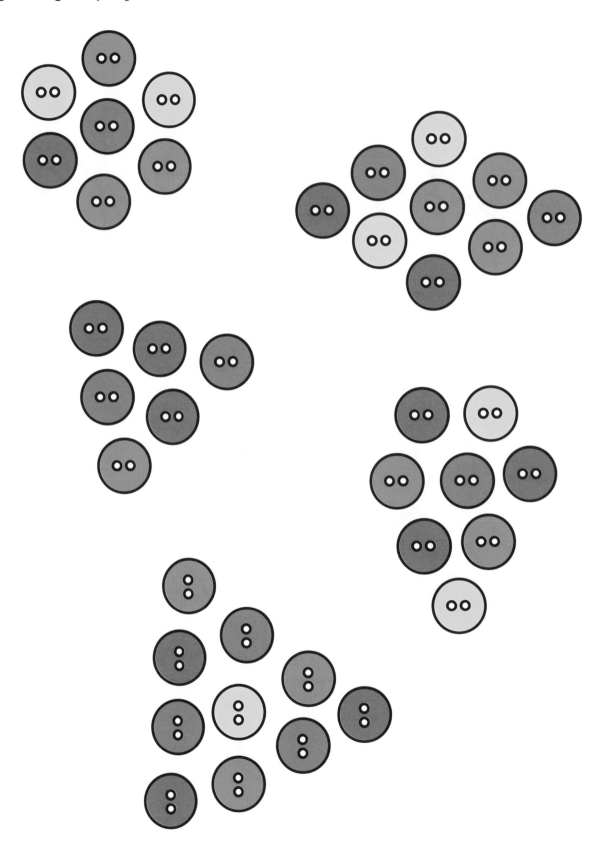

Ring the numbers that match the pictures.

6 7 8 9 10

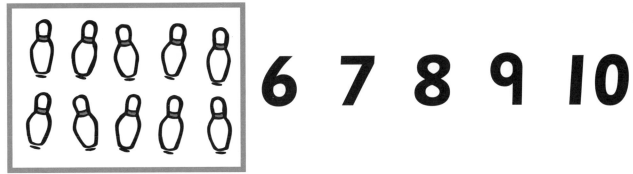

6 7 8 9 10

6 7 8 9 10

6 7 8 9 10

Children have a natural curiosity about numbers and this needs to be encouraged in the following ways ...

- **talk about significant personal numbers:**
  e.g. your child's age or your house number.

- **explain how numbers are useful to us:**
  e.g. the numbers of the TV channels, bus numbers, car registration numbers.

- **find opportunities to use number language:**
  e.g. "how many altogether", "one more", "one less", "the number before", "the number after", etc.

- **compare numbers,** e.g. which number is larger?

- **talk about the names of very large numbers:**
  e.g. hundreds, thousands.

Let's go!

Say the car numbers in order.
Write the numbers on the cars.

Ring the group of ten triangles.

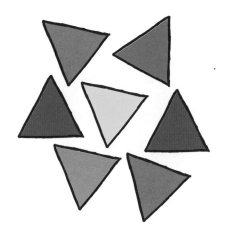

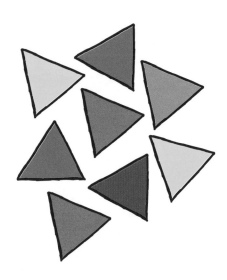

Draw lines to join the pictures to the numbers.

7

10

9

Put the numbers in the right order.
Draw them on the board.

Join the dots. Start at 0.
Count to 10.

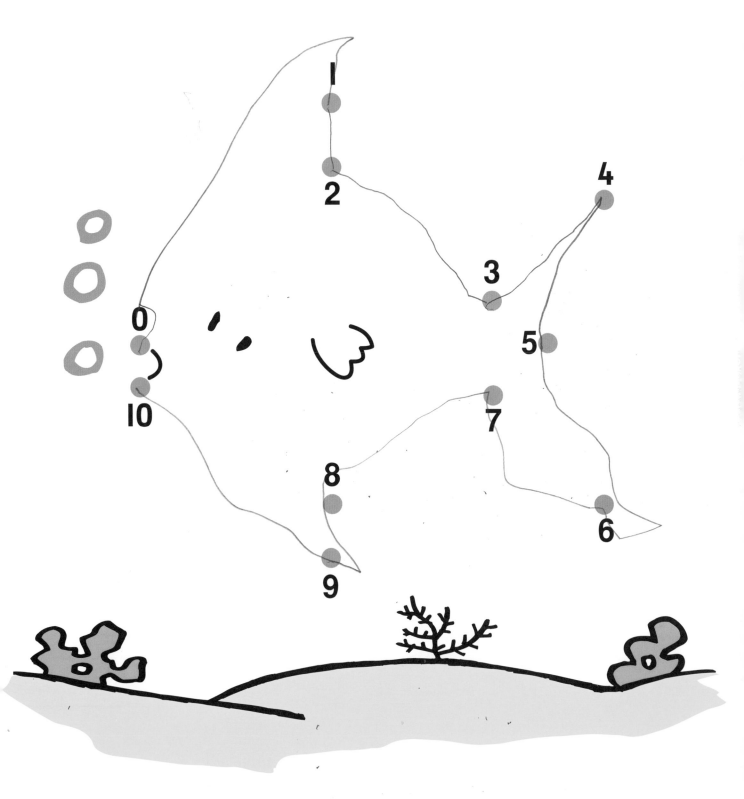

How many shoes?

How many socks?

Draw more socks to match the shoes.

Ring the numbers that match the pictures.

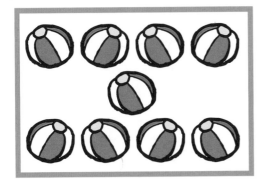

6 7 8 9 10

6 7 8 9 10

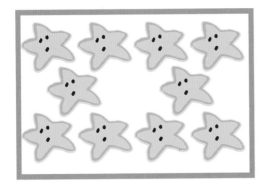

6 7 8 9 10

6 7 8 9 10

Draw one more picture in each row.
Write how many altogether in each box.

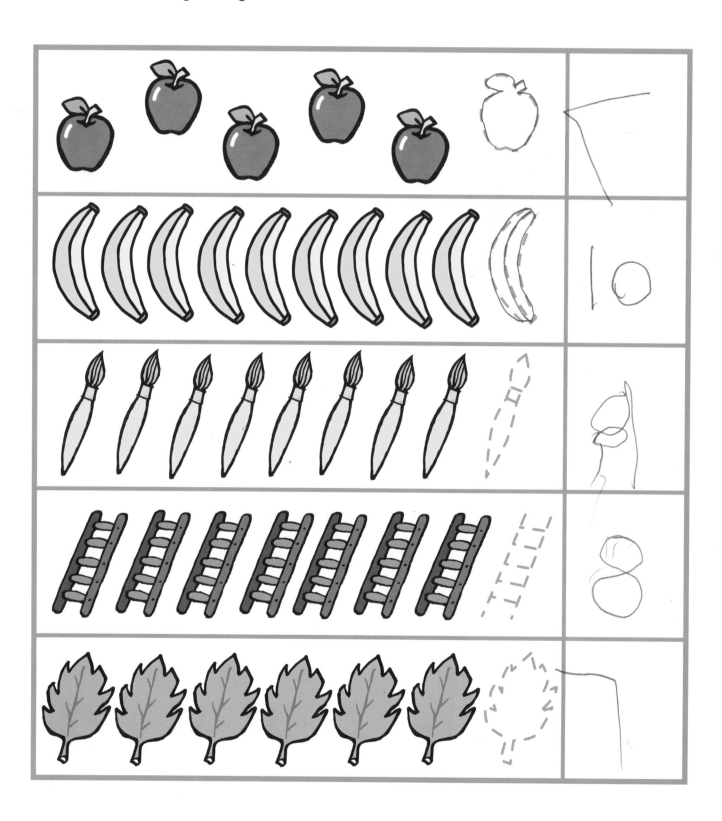

Draw more shapes in each row.
The number of shapes must match the number in each box.

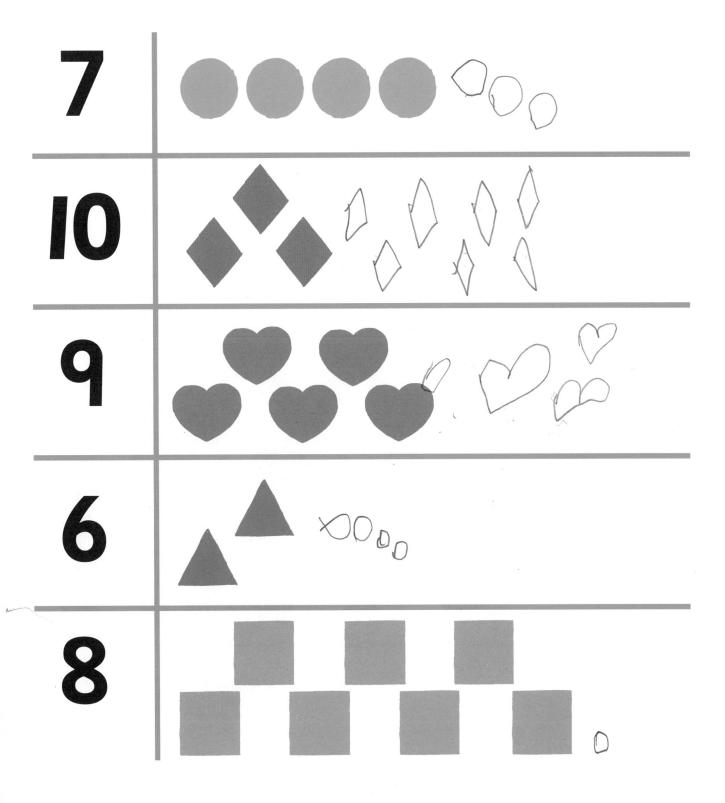

The clown has ten balls.
Write the numbers from one to ten on the balls.

Count the ladybirds in each group.
Write the number in each box.

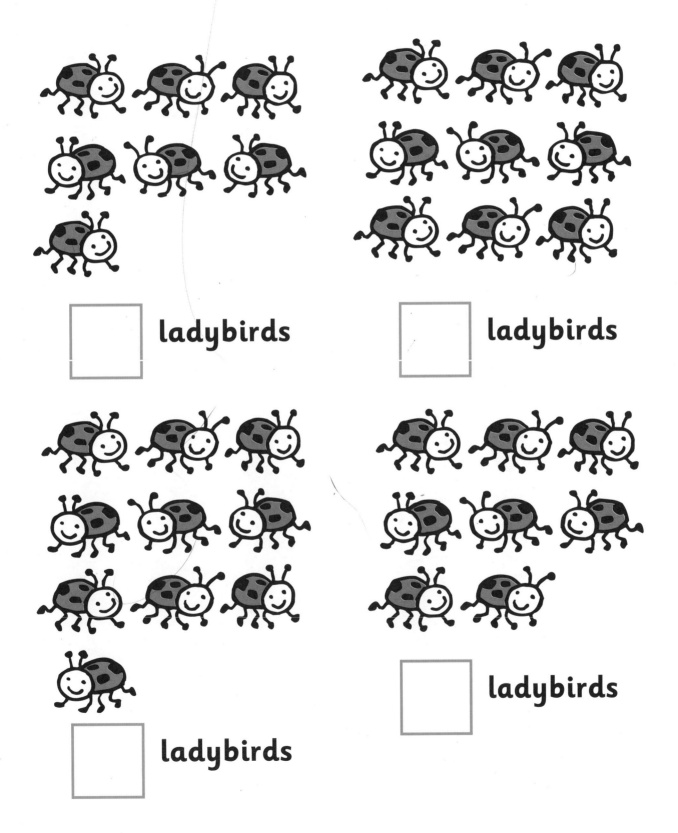

ladybirds

ladybirds

ladybirds

ladybirds

There are ten steps to climb.
Write ten numbers, in order, on the steps.

Draw one more shape in each row.
Write how many altogether in each box.

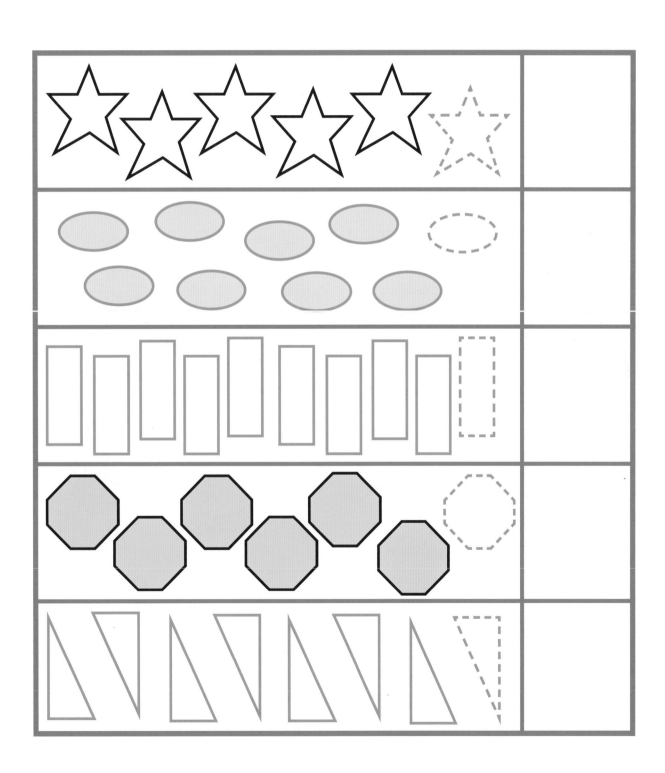

Learn to write the number 11

Follow the lines to write the number eleven.

Count eleven footballers.

Colour eleven beads red.
Colour the others blue.

Write the numbers.

 red beads   **blue beads**

Follow the lines to write the number twelve.

Count twelve bottles.

Colour ten cabbages.
Draw two more.

How many altogether?

 **cabbages**

Count 10 rabbits.
Draw two more rabbits.

How many altogether?

 rabbits

Draw more fish in the pond to make 12 altogether.
Count the trees.

trees

Follow the lines to write the number thirteen.

13 13 13

Draw some more apples to make thirteen.

Colour thirteen bricks yellow.
Colour the others green.

Write the numbers.

 yellow bricks **green bricks**

Follow the lines to write the number fourteen.

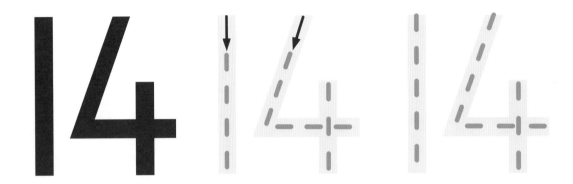

Count fourteen frogs.

Colour fourteen socks green.
Colour the others pink.

Write the numbers.

 green socks   **pink socks**

Follow the lines to write the number fifteen.

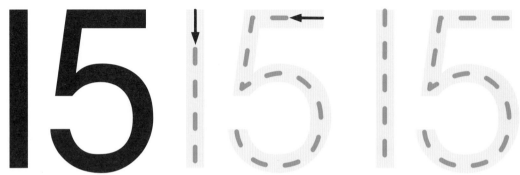

Count fifteen petals.

Colour ten squares.
Draw five more.

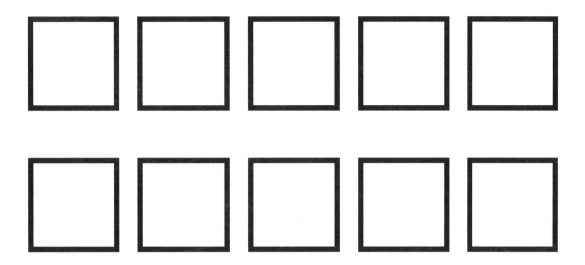

How many altogether?

 **squares**

Say the rocket numbers in order.

Write the numbers on the rockets.

Count 10 birds.
Draw 5 more birds.

How many altogether? **birds**

Everyday activities might involve:

- **setting the table at mealtimes for one more (addition) or for one less (subtraction), sharing biscuits or treats equally between children (division), estimating how many sandwiches to make for a party (multiplication).**
- **sorting and grouping objects,** *e.g. finding all the socks from the washing and then putting them into pairs.*
- **arranging objects in rows to help counting,** *e.g. eggs in egg boxes.*
- **"counting on" from a number rather than starting from one each time.**

5 9 2

Let's go!

Draw one egg for each chicken.
Count the eggs.

eggs

Count the skittles.
Draw 5 more skittles.

How many altogether?

 skittles

The trains are in order.
Write in the missing number.

Write in the missing numbers on the trucks.

Follow the lines to write the number sixteen.

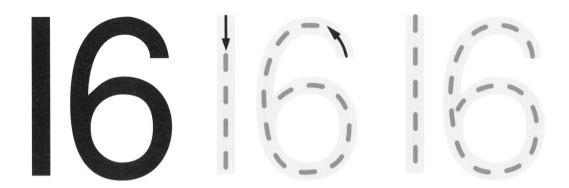

Count sixteen milk bottles.

Colour ten triangles.
Draw six more.

How many altogether? **triangles**

Draw more shells to match the numbers.

12

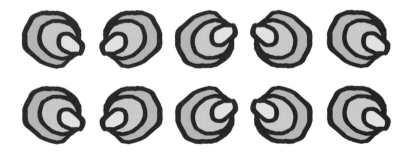

13

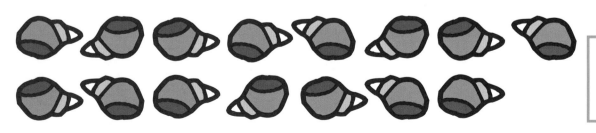

16

Count the triangles.

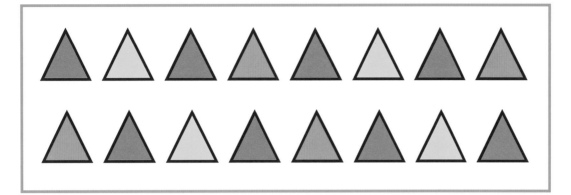

Count the squares.

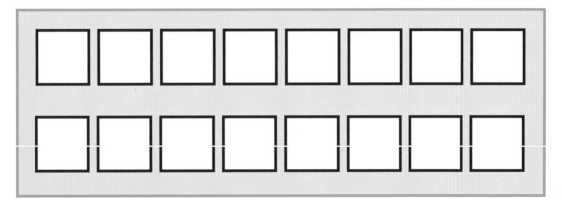

Draw sixteen circles.

How many?

 **squares**  **triangles**

Follow the lines to write the number seventeen.

Count seventeen leaves.

Count the crocodile's teeth.
Draw some more teeth to make 17.

How many altogether?

 **teeth**

Learn to write the number 18

Follow the lines to write the number eighteen.

18 18 8

Count eighteen cars.

Colour the oranges.
Draw eight more oranges.

How many altogether?

oranges

Count 13 shirts.
Draw 5 more shirts.

How many altogether? **shirts**

Count 10 sweets.
Draw 8 more sweets.

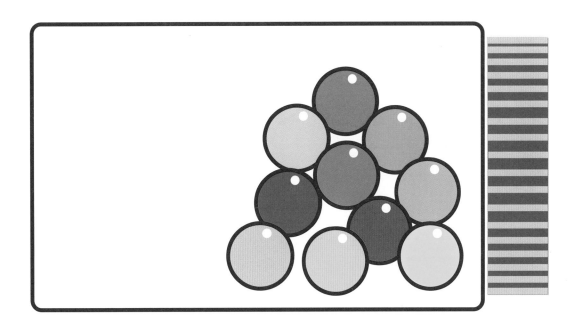

Count the pieces of chocolate. **pieces**

Follow the lines to write the number nineteen.

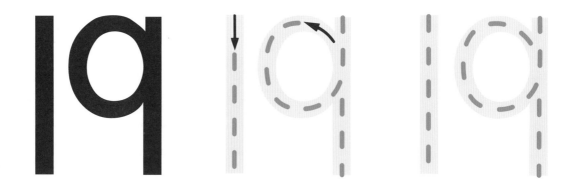

Count nineteen drums.

Colour nineteen trees green.
Colour any others brown.

Write the numbers.

 **green
trees**

 **brown
trees**

Follow the lines to write the number twenty.

Count twenty candles.

Colour ten buttons.
Draw ten more buttons.

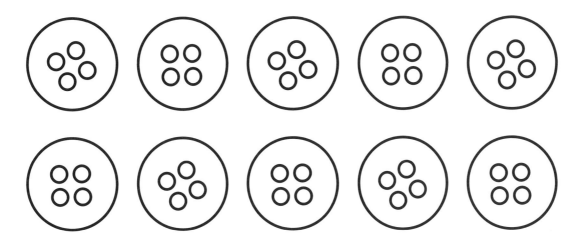

How many altogether?

 **buttons**

Order numbers, count to 20

Say the shirt numbers in order.
Write the numbers on the shirts.

Count 20 balloons.
Draw a cloud over one balloon.
How many can you see now?

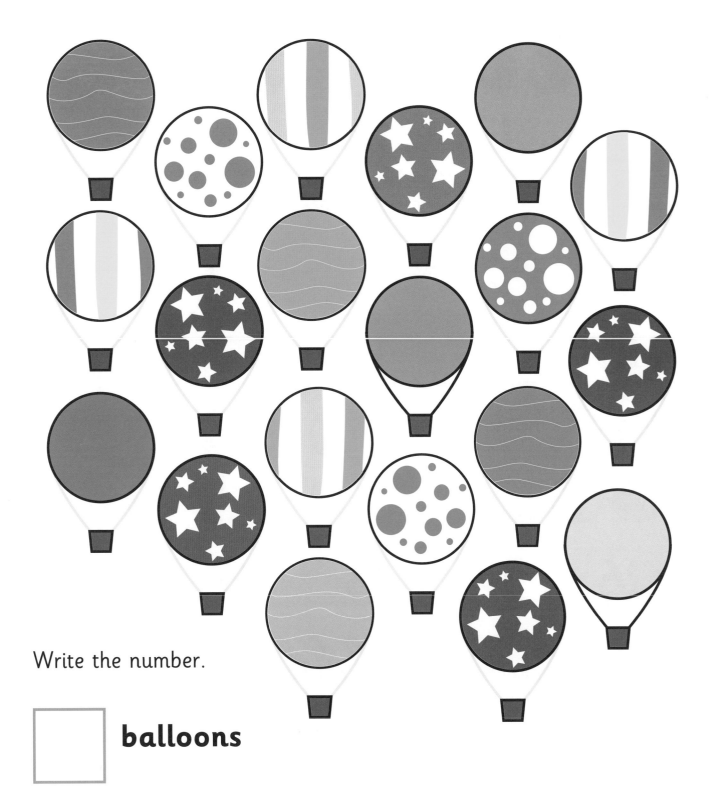

Write the number.

balloons

Ring the numbers that match the pictures.

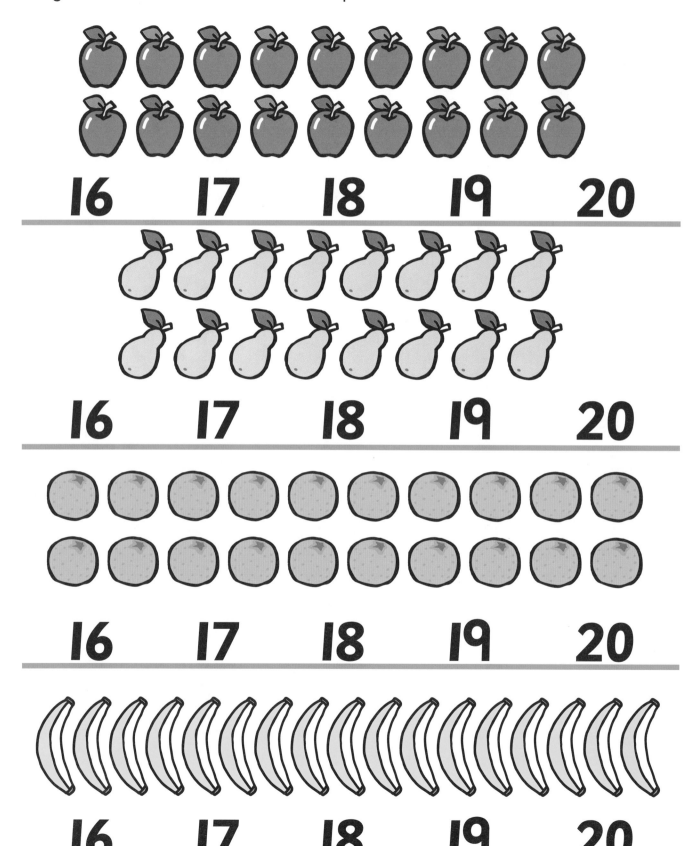

16   17   18   19   20

16   17   18   19   20

16   17   18   19   20

16   17   18   19   20

Frog jumps along the path in twos.
Write the numbers the frog jumps on.

2	4								

Count in 3s, count in 4s

Kangaroo jumps along the path in threes.
Write the numbers the kangaroo jumps on.

| 3 | 6 | | | | |

Start

Dinosaur jumps along the path in fours.
Write the numbers the dinosaur jumps on.

| 4 | | | | |

Start

zero	ten
one	eleven
two	twelve
three	thirteen
four	fourteen
five	fifteen
six	sixteen
seven	seventeen
eight	eighteen
nine	nineteen
	twenty

count
match
altogether
number

Tick the boxes to show what you know!
Now I can ...

☐ **count up to 5 objects**

☐ count up to 10 objects

☐ **count up to 15 objects**

☐ count up to 20 objects

☐ **point to the pictures, or objects, as I count**

☐ say the numbers 0 to 10 in the correct order

☐ **say the numbers 0 to 20 in the correct order**

☐ write the numbers 0 to 10

☐ **write the numbers 11 to 20**

☐ match numbers to pictures

☐ **add one more to a number**

☐ add more to make a number

☐ **recognise numbers 0 to 10**

☐ recognise numbers 0 to 20

Look out for
the companion title:
Mega English 3–5

Mega English (3–5)
ISBN 978 1 4052 2011 8

Look out for **MEGA Maths** and
MEGA English for 5–7 year-olds, too!

Mega English (5–7)
ISBN 978 1 4052 2013 2

Mega Maths (5–7)
ISBN 978 1 4052 2014 9

Each book is packed with 128 pages of learning exercises and
100 fun stickers to enjoy.

All titles comply with the National Curriculum (England and Wales) and
English and Mathematics 5–14 (Scotland) and are in line with the
Curriculum guidance for the Foundation Stage, and the National Literacy
and Numeracy Strategies.

**These are the perfect books to help support your child's
progress through primary school.**